# FATHERHOOD:
## THE **MANLIEST** PROFESSION

OTHER BOOKS AND AUDIO BOOKS

BY MATTHEW BUCKLEY

*Chickens in the Headlights*

*Bullies in the Headlights*

*To Brian, We want to honor you for being such a great Dad and such a loving Son, Happy Fathers Day! We Love you, Dad & Sharon*

# FATHERHOOD:
## THE **MANLIEST** PROFESSION

Hilarious Stories
Inspired by a Dad's
Real-Life Experiences

# MATTHEW BUCKLEY

Covenant Communications, Inc.

Cover image: Fatherhood copyright © 2013 by Nate Call. For more information, go to http://www. callnate.blogspot.com.

Cover design copyright © 2013 by Covenant Communications, Inc.

Published by Covenant Communications, Inc.
American Fork, Utah

Printed in the United States of America
First Printing: April 2013

19 18 17 16 15 14 13     10 9 8 7 6 5 4 3 2 1

ISBN 978-1-62108-431-0

This book is dedicated to Spencer, John, Steven, Jared, and Isaac—five boys who made me a father and make me want to be a better father.

I will always be your dad.

# ACKNOWLEDGMENTS

THIS BOOK WOULDN'T HAVE HAPPENED if my editor, Samantha Millburn, hadn't approached me at a conference and thrown out the idea during dinner.

"There are a lot of . . . feel-good Father's Day books. Books that are inspirational. Uplifting. Books that touch the heart and move the soul. But I think that what the market might need is something with more . . ."

I burped, wiped my mouth with my sleeve, and spat on the floor. "Something with more potty humor?"

I knew Samantha loved the idea by the way she shook her head and said no. We talked about a Father's Day book filled with humor. Not potty humor, but the kind of humor that comes when dads stand around and swap stories—crazy stories—of what it's like to be a father.

My mind was racing by the end of the conference. I'd jotted down some story ideas, and within days, I'd started writing. As I talked with friends and family, more stories came. I loved hearing how different fathers can be, and yet how similar we all are.

I hope this book is received in the spirit it is given. Fatherhood is work. Fatherhood is hard. There are times when we wonder if we have it in us to finish the race. But fatherhood is also one of the most fulfilling, fun, crazy, wonderful experiences on the planet. The purpose of this book is to remind us just how fun it can be.

I would like to especially thank my writing group—Cory Webb, Margot Hovley, Chris Miller, Ken Lee, Kendra Fowler, Christy Monson, and Janette Wright. I am forever in their debt for their keen eyes, their insight, and their words of encouragement.

I would also like to thank Mindi Larson Barker, Jaime Theler, and her husband, Jason Theler, for inviting me to my first Ragnar and providing stories that ended up in this book.

I would also like to thank my father, who is a writer and a poet himself.

# INTRODUCTION

THIS BOOK IS FOR MEN.

Not just any men. A rare kind of men—the manliest of men—lumberjacks.

Wait. That's not right. Not lumberjacks. I meant to say *fathers*. That's right. Fathers.

Fatherhood is not an endeavor for the faint of heart. Only the boldest of bold should apply. You can't be squeamish because there are diapers involved, and not the starched and crisp linen diapers. Diapers after they've been used, if you catch my drift. You'll definitely catch their drift.

Being a father means you have to think fast on your feet. You must be judicious, wise, brave, tender, and willing to put on a frilly hat and sit down to a pretend tea party.

Fact: Of all the parents on the planet, only about half of them have what it takes to be a father.

That's right. You heard me. Only half.

As a parent, there are many things vying for our attention. We must partner with our wives to acquire, prepare, and put food on the table. There are lawns that never stop growing until the snow flies (then you get to put away the lawn mower and pull out the snow shovel). There is a home to be maintained. Power tools to be fired up and used with appropriate grunting sounds. Vehicular maintenance that must be performed.

And on top of all of this, there are other things that must be done. Father things. Important things: the Band-Aid that must be applied in just the right manner or the pain won't go away, the sports event or artistic performance that cannot happen without your presence, the bedtime stories that must be read with the appropriate silly voices, the babies who need to be welcomed into this world and protected while they grow, sons who need to learn the lessons of manhood, daughters who need to learn the lessons of womanhood, and perhaps most important of all, raising children who know how to love others.

Fatherhood is not for the weak. It's not for the clueless or the afraid. It is challenging, and it is rewarding.

This book is for those bold enough to toss everything else aside, grab the experience of fatherhood with both hands, and hang on for the ride of your lives.

This book is not meant to instruct because you can't contain everything you need to know about being a father in a single book. There are a million ways to be a good father. There are a million things you need to know. Luckily, you're a man and you already know everything.

This book is not meant to inspire. Inspiration is only needed when you feel too weak to do anything. Do you feel too weak to do anything? I didn't think so.

This book is meant only to remind. To remind you how *awesome* you are because you're a man and because you're a dad.

This book is for the men and boys who have ever looked at a difficult task—maybe even an impossible task—and said, "Oh yeah, I can do that."

This book is for the men and boys who are now, or hope one day to become, a father.

## Conversations in Fatherhood

Father: Did you know that every time you hit your brother, a puppy dies?

7yo: Hmmmm . . . What if you hit your brother with a stick?

5yo: Then a dolphin dies.

# CHAPTER 1

I'M A FATHER. I HAVE five sons. My five sons watch me and follow me and learn from me. Usually this is a good thing.

Sometimes it's not.

I'm an author. I write funny books. In my second book, *Bullies in the Headlights*, I reference a primary song that is often sung in primary sharing times across the nation. The original words are about two hands that are being very reverent, quiet, and obedient.

In the book, I changed the words to the following:

*I have five little fingers on one of my hands,*
*I have six on the other, I don't understand.*
*During all the long hours till daylight is through,*
*I have one little finger with nothing to do.*

I also described actions that go along with the new words, one of these actions involving sticking one's fingers up one's nose. My sons, of course, have read my book. They happen to like my version of the song better.

My boys have sung my version so many times they've forgotten the original words. At family home evening, at primary, whenever the song is sung, they sing my version and do my actions.

We were moving, and it was our last week at church. My wife and I both taught primary. As it so happened, all five of my boys were also in primary. One of our ward's traditions was something called *Heartfelt Songs*. At the beginning of the year, all of the children wrote down their favorite primary song on a slip of paper. Each week, the chorister picked one of the slips of paper. The child who picked that song got to come up to the front and lead the rest of the primary.

I sat in my small chair, watching each of the kids in my primary class like a hawk—waiting to shush them or move them around to keep the peace. Then I heard the announcement.

"It's the Buckleys' last week," the chorister said. "And it just so happens that all five of them have the same heartfelt song—'I Have Two Little Hands.' So we want all five of them to come up and lead us in the song."

I should mention I was sitting right up in the front.

My five boys walked to the front of the room. They looked a little nervous. I glanced over my shoulder and could see my wife giving all five boys the stink eye. I knew exactly what she was saying as sure as if she'd yelled it from the back of the room.

*If you sing the wrong version and do the wrong actions, you will never eat dinner again.*

I turned back to my boys. I could tell by the looks on their faces they understood exactly the meaning behind Mom's stink eye.

The pianist played. The children in the primary sang. My boys stood there like prisoners waiting to be shot. They couldn't remember the real words.

"Well," the chorister said, sounding a little confused since none of them had actually sung. "Can you boys tell us why that's your favorite song?"

Son number three was quick to fill in the details. "My dad changed all the words and actions, so we like to sing it. Only we couldn't this time because . . ." He pointed at my wife.

There were a few seconds of silence, and then the chorister looked at me. "Well then, why don't we ask Brother Buckley to come up and teach us his way?"

My turn to look like a deer in the headlights.

I didn't even need to look at my wife. "I don't know if my version would exactly set the right spirit," I said. "I think the version we just sang is perfect."

The chorister nodded but continued to look confused. My kids hustled back to their seats, and sharing time got back on track.

I sat in my chair, feeling the weight of fatherhood resting firmly on my shoulders.

Conversations in Fatherhood

Voicemail from the 5yo: "Hi, Dad. Walter was carrying me down the stairs, and he dropped me. I fell on my head. I think I'm bleeding. Wait . . . Let me check." Fifteen seconds of phone noise. "Nope. I'm not bleeding. Just a big red mark. Bye."

# CHAPTER 2

*One night when I was just a little boy, my father threatened to spank me. He never did. Thirty years later, I stood in my boys' bedroom and made threats of my own. Not spanking, but classical music. I took those two experiences and combined them into a single story. That story became the first chapter in my first book—*Chickens in the Headlights.

DAD STOOD IN THE MIDDLE of our bedroom, strategically positioned so each boy could both see and hear him. My brothers and I lay on our beds, trying to look humbled and repentant. Peter was hiding under the covers in hopes that if he could not see Dad, then maybe Dad could not see him.

Dad spoke in that quiet voice parents do so well, a low sound that still carries tremendous emotion. I could tell he wanted to come right out and yell but was restraining himself so as not to wake the baby.

He was mad.

"How many times do your mother and I have to send you to bed?" he asked, his voice taking on a distinct pleading ring.

I was old enough to know a rhetorical question when I heard one, but Peter had not quite figured it out. His muffled reply came from under the covers. "I don't know. Maybe six times?" he guessed.

My father smacked his own forehead, and I could hear him muttering something under his breath.

"*No!*" he finally sputtered, a bit louder than before. The lump of covers that was Peter fell back against the wall. "I don't want to hear another sound from this room, or there will be some serious consequences!"

In addition to the fault of not knowing whether a question should or should not be answered, Peter also had to know the consequences of any given forbidden action. He liked to weigh the pleasures of disobedience with the pains of punishment.

"What will the consequences be, Daddy?" the blanket asked.

The talking lump of blankets seemed to calm Dad down a little. His voice took on the air of a judge passing sentence. "The consequences of getting out of bed again," Dad said, "will be that I'll turn off your music."

Every night, one of us chose music to help us fall asleep. Tonight was my turn, and we were all enjoying some nursery rhymes sung by kids who sounded far too happy for their own good. On Sundays, our parents made us listen to Primary songs or hymns, and on Saturdays, Dad chose the music. Nobody liked Saturday's selections.

"So what if we get out of bed two times?" Peter asked, wanting to weigh all of his options.

"Then I'll turn on Vivaldi!" Dad replied, his voice raising just a hair. We all complained when we had to listen to Four Seasons. In spite of the darkness, I could see Dad's face turning red. His temper was beginning to flare.

"What if we get out of bed three times?"

"Then I'll turn it up!" he hissed. Then, forgetting about our sleeping brothers (Simon, Peter, and I shared the room with our brothers John and Jacob. John, who was almost five, and Jacob, who was three, had already fallen asleep), he yelled, "Good night!"

Spinning on his heels, Dad stormed out of the room. Although Dad gets upset in front of us from time to time, if he's really going to blow his stack, he does it somewhere else.

After Dad's stomping faded downstairs, my older brother, Simon, leaned down from his upper bunk. "Hey, Matthew," he whispered. "If somebody *yells* good night to you, do you think they really want you to have a good night?"

I giggled into my pillow. Dad's pleas and lectures had not stopped the night's festivities, only interrupted them.

To be fair, we hadn't gone to bed very well. We'd snuck out once, and my parents had sent us back to bed. We had then tiptoed, crawled, and even scooted on our bellies. Each time, we were caught and returned to bed. We pulled out every excuse in the book to get out of bed, including the one where we claimed our toenails were too long and were catching on the sheets. The last time, Dad personally escorted us back to see us climb into bed.

I lay in bed and looked around the room. There was comfortable clutter almost everywhere. Clothes hung on dresser drawers, shoes spilled out of full closets, toys lay scattered throughout the room—all this despite the fact that we had cleaned today. In fairness, you couldn't expect a whole lot of order in a bedroom shared by five boys. And for that matter, you really couldn't expect much in the sleep department either.

I wondered for a moment if Dad's lecture had been enough to finally settle us down. I looked over at Peter. Hanging upside down from the bar that spanned the upper bunk, he did not look like he was anywhere near drifting off to sleep.

Simon, who slept above me, peeked his head over the side. He looked back and forth at the floor by our bunk bed. His eyes darted around the room, and his forehead wrinkled. It took me a moment to realize what was happening. My heart beat just a little bit quicker.

Simon had a plan.

Peter stopped swinging to hear him out. We listened attentively, and by the time Simon finished explaining his idea, Peter and I were both in cahoots. For some reason, we always seemed to forget that his ideas ended up getting us into trouble. He could sell us on anything.

This new project called for a lot of pillows. Many of Simon's ideas called for pillows as a safety measure. It was nice that Simon took measures against any physical mishaps, since Peter or I usually tried the idea first.

We sent Peter on the pillow-gathering mission, and in a few short minutes, he returned with pillows stacked up so high all we could see was a tuft of blond hair sticking up like a periscope.

"Peter, are those all of the pillows?" Simon asked. He and I had both jumped out of bed and now stood on the floor in our one-piece pajamas. "Did you get the spare ones out of the closet?"

"The only pillows in the whole house that I didn't get are the ones on the couch," Peter declared. His voice was muffled behind the pillows. "And I'm not gonna ask Mom and Dad to stand up so I can get those."

"Never mind the couch pillows," Simon said. "We have enough with these."

Peter, Simon, and I each grabbed a hold of my bunk bed. Simon counted to three, and we pulled.

SCREEEK. The bed slid out twelve inches from the wall. We froze, each of us still bent over with our hands on the bed. The noise had been low-pitched but loud.

"What in the . . ." My Dad's rumbling voice floated up from downstairs. "Honey, was that you?"

"It wasn't me," Mom answered from the kitchen. "I think it came from upstairs."

Footsteps crossed the floor, and we heard our father's voice yell up the stairs. "Boys? What did I just say? Are you trying to send your father to the nuthouse?"

Mom took over, sensing my father was near his breaking point. When it came to parenting, they made a good tag team.

"Boys, are you in bed?" Mom called up in a voice that told us quite clearly she knew we were not but that we had better get there fast if we still wanted to be on the earth when the sun rose in the morning.

None of us dared come right out and lie to Mom or Dad, so all three of us promptly jumped onto my lower bunk and yelled in unison, "Yes, Mom!" Simon went a bit further than the rest of us, adding, "Sheesh, I was almost asleep!" Simon had explained long ago that when you looked at the big picture, like an entire week or month, the fact that he would be asleep in two hours constituted being "almost asleep" and, hence, was not technically a lie.

"Okay, I don't want to hear any more noises," she called up.

My father, wanting to throw his last two bits in, hollered up after her. "If I have to come up there one more time, you boys will all have sore bottoms in the morning."

We sat still for a few minutes, none of us thinking for a moment of not going through with the plan. After a few more minutes, things settled down again, so we quietly began to work. We grabbed pillows and began to stuff them between the wall and the bed. Peter had done his job well, and by the time we were done, the pillows were stacked halfway up the wall. It must have looked safer than usual because Simon tried it first.

He climbed up onto the top bed, lay straight on it, then rolled off the side between the bed and the wall. He dropped three feet, landed on the pillows, and rolled onto the lower bunk. He ended up on his back, the wide grin on his face telling Peter and me all we needed to know. For ten solid minutes, we climbed, fell, rolled, and shoved each other, trying to be the first one back to the top.

After awhile, we began to try different ways—feet first, headfirst, or curled up in a ball. Then Simon came up with another idea. "Let's get Jacob!"

Jacob was brother number five. The funny thing about Jacob was that when he fell asleep, he slept hard. Nothing could wake him up. Short of having someone dump water on him, Jacob slept through anything.

Simon went over to the crib and picked up Jacob. He threw him over his shoulder and began to climb up the ladder to the top bunk. Jacob's arms fell down over his head, and his head bounced against Simon's back. Peter and I began to chuckle.

Simon got to the top and dropped Jacob to the bed. "Load the torpedoes!" Simon whispered in a funny voice. "Torpedoes loaded and ready, sir," he whispered in another crazy voice. "Fire!"

Peter and I began to laugh.

Jacob dropped like a sack of potatoes, bounced off the pillows, rolled across the lower bunk, and fell with a thump onto the hardwood floor.

He slept on, oblivious.

Peter bent over, trying to suppress his laughter by curling up in a ball on the floor. His laughter was contagious.

"Again! Again!" I whispered through my giggles.

Simon hopped off the bunk, picked Jacob up, and climbed up the ladder again. Halfway up, Jacob began to slip off his back. Simon grabbed the foot of his pajamas and was barely able to hang on. Once he was on top again, he repeated the process: drop, roll, thump. I looked for a pillow to laugh into, but they were all being used.

Peter got on the lower bunk and rearranged the pillows. He piled several pillows in such a way that they gave Jacob a nice sliding ramp.

Simon hauled Jacob up again, rolled him across the top bunk, and dropped him. This time, Jacob did not fall to the floor with a bump. He rolled down the ramp Peter had made, skidded across the floor, and bumped into our nightstand.

The lamp on the nightstand teetered, and for a brief moment, I thought it would right itself. Wishful thinking. It fell to the floor with a deafening crash. We froze.

I looked at Jacob. He was still asleep, and I noticed that he was sucking his thumb with a contented smile on his face.

I turned to look at Peter, who had a scared look on his face. Our only hope was that Dad had *M\*A\*S\*H* on too loud to hear the crash. No such luck.

We heard the dreaded words reverberate from downstairs. "That's it! I've had it! I'm coming up to spank some bottoms!"

Dad rarely spanked us. Sure, we got a swat every once in a while, but never a good thrashing. Dad was normally a pretty calm person, so when he got upset enough to spank us, we knew we had gone a bit too far.

I began to panic. We needed an idea, a plan that could turn the situation in our favor.

Simon!

Simon always had ideas. I turned to the top bunk, where Simon had just rolled Jacob off. Moments before, he had been perched like a gargoyle, watching the events unfold below. Now he lay curled up on his bed, feigning sleep. I couldn't believe it! The whole thing was his idea, and now Peter and I were stuck with the mess!

For some reason, it didn't occur to me to hop into bed and pretend I was asleep as well.

Before I looked away, I noticed—feeling part admiration and part loathing—that Simon had even had the presence of mind to let a little spittle fall out of his mouth onto his pillow. That little touch could have fooled anyone.

The stinker.

I looked back at Peter, who was crossing his legs and hopping from one foot to the other. Almost every time Peter got overly nervous, he suddenly needed to use the bathroom. While funny most of the time, this tendency could sometimes be a hindrance. Wide-eyed and frightened, he looked like he was about to crack.

"Calm down, Peter," I said in what I hoped was a soothing voice.

"What do we do?" Peter asked, his voice filled with dread. "Dad's going to spank us for sure."

I looked around the room. Simon had abandoned us, so it was up to me.

"We could hide in the bathroom," I suggested. Our bedroom adjoined the upstairs bathroom, and we could sneak into it without having to actually leave the safety of our room.

"Dad has the key," Peter said, his voice cracking under the pressure.

I looked around. I could think of nothing.

"Let's hide under the bed!" Peter suggested, and for a moment, I thought his idea just might work. It didn't take long for me to see the flaws in his plan.

"Dad is too smart for that. He'd look for us there," I explained. "Besides, we cleaned our room today, so there's not room for anything else under there."

Peter got a wild look in his eyes, and then I saw that he had lost it. He ran to his bed, pulled the covers over his head, and didn't move. Peter liked to play tough, but when push came to shove, he was definitely a softie.

I stood in the middle of the room, figuring that the least I could do was throw Jacob back into his crib. I grabbed the foot of his pajamas and dragged him to the crib; he left a line of drool across the floor. With a quick heave, Jacob was back inside. Now at least we wouldn't get in trouble for using our brother as a torpedo.

I was turning to jump back into my own bed when, out of the corner of my eye, I saw the bookcase next to my bed. Inspiration struck. It was one of those moments you usually just hear about, and in my mind's eye, I saw the solution as clear as anything I had ever seen before in my short life.

I ran to the bookcase and grabbed a book. Unzipping my pajamas, I shoved the book in and around to the back. After a bit of adjusting, the book lay squarely over my rear end. Peter must have calmed down enough to peek out from under his covers.

"What the . . . What are you doing?" his muffled voice asked.

I figured a demonstration was better than an explanation. I reached around and whacked my own backside. "See?" I told him, a bit proud of my obvious brilliance. "It doesn't hurt a bit. Well, it hurts the hand a little, but that will be Dad's."

The lump of blankets stayed still for a moment, but then suddenly, Peter reappeared. He dashed across the room, grabbed a book, and raced back to his bed. He dove under the covers, but I could see some wriggling as he followed my example.

I hopped into bed and pulled the covers up over my smile. I could not wait for the swift hand of justice to meet my new-and-improved armored bottom. I pictured Dad coming into my room, yelling and screaming, then after trying to swat me, recoiling and grabbing his hand in pain. Oh, how sweet it would be. I waited . . .

Simon never got back up, and Peter eventually came out for air. John stirred in his sleep, and Jacob slept on as deeply as ever. I kept waiting, but eventually, my eyelids became heavy, and I drifted off to sleep, *The Cat in the Hat* pressed firmly against my bottom.

# Conversations in Fatherhood

5yo: You know what I want on Christmas Day?

Dad: What?

5yo: A bad dream.

Dad: What? Why would you want that?

5yo: So I can wake up early! I hope it's one where Santa comes down the chimney with a shotgun.

# CHAPTER 3

"*Gregory Scott!*"

Mom was calling me, and she didn't sound happy.

*Stupid Jimmy.*

It wasn't my fault. Really. But you can't exactly ignore your mom when she's calling. Well, I mean, you can, but when she has to track you down, she's even madder. Far better to walk into a storm than to wait for the storm to come to you.

"Coming, Mother!" I shouted, and then I didn't move. If I went up right away, Mom might still be mad. Better to let her cool down for a few minutes. Of course, if I waited too long, that would only make her more upset.

Timing was everything.

I walked slowly up the stairs, taking heavy steps. I hoped Mom would hear me coming and my obedience would calm her down. Jimmy was at the top of the staircase, a smug look on his face.

"Stupid head," I said under my breath.

"You're in big trouble," Jimmy said. "Mom's going to make you vacuum."

"Triple-double stupid head," I said again and walked past him. I knew he was still looking at me, so I bent over and shook my bottom at him.

"Mom!" Jimmy shouted. "Greg just mooned me!"

"Liar!" I yelled over my shoulder, making sure my voice carried with it a healthy degree of shock and indignation. I knew that to truly moon somebody, you had to pull your pants down. I hadn't mooned him; I'd simply used my completely covered buttocks to communicate feelings of disdain.

I found Mother sitting on the couch, holding a book but not reading it. She shook her head from side to side as if she were watching a tennis match in slow motion. She looked relatively calm. If I played my cards right, I might get out of this without too much more than a scolding.

"What, Mom?" Rule number one: admit nothing. If you're charged with a crime, let the prosecutor bring it up. Perhaps she didn't know what I'd done.

"Did you spit carrots at your brother?"

Rats.

My first line of defense was always to look for a loophole. Sometimes I could get off by defining a word in a unique way or liberally changing the meaning of a question. But at the moment, I could think of nothing. I'd had a mouthful of carrots, and I had, in fact, spit them at my brother. Getting off on a technicality wouldn't work this time. Luckily, I had an excellent reason for my actions.

"Yes. I spit carrots at Jimmy. But, Mom—"

Mom held up her hand. I knew better than to keep talking. Mom was calming down quite a bit now. Things might be landing in my favor, even if I didn't get to tell my side of the story. I lowered my head, hoping I was striking a pose of humility and repentance. I wanted to look like a good son, ready to be taught a valuable life lesson from a wise and loving mother.

"Sweetheart," Mom said. "I know you want to tell me what Jimmy did that made you spit carrots at him."

"Yes," I said. "As a matter of fact—"

"But you see," she continued as if I hadn't said a word, "it doesn't matter. It never matters. Do you remember what Jesus taught?"

Rats again. It was hard to argue when she brought church into the mix. "Like when Jesus made a whip and went to the temple so He could whack those one guys—"

"No." Mom shook her head. "He said love your enemy. Bless those that curse you. Turn the other cheek. Can't you see? Whatever Jimmy did, you can still love him. You can ignore him or give him a hug and tell him you are glad to be his brother."

I think if I'd hugged Jimmy, he'd have punched me in the neck.

"You need to understand that what you learn in Sunday School isn't just nice information. It's something that will help you be a better person. It will help you lead a happier life."

There was nothing I could say. Even telling my side of the story wouldn't help. What was I going to do, try to find a hole in the teachings of Christ? They'd stood up for two thousand years. I didn't think I'd find a loophole on a Thursday afternoon that allowed me to spit carrots at my brother. Best just to nod and say I understood.

I nodded. "I understand."

"Will you try to be a better boy? The next time you get mad at Jimmy, will you stop and think to yourself, *what would Jesus do?* Will you do that for your mother?"

I nodded again.

Mom smiled. "I love you, Greg. Now, Jimmy says there are little bits of carrot all over the carpet downstairs. Go get the vacuum and get it cleaned up."

"But, Mom!" I protested. "Don't I even get to tell my side of the story?"

Mom sat back and opened her book. "What does Jesus say about honoring your parents?"

I knew I'd been beat. I folded my arms. I guess when I looked at the big picture, it could have been worse. All I had to do was vacuum. Sometimes Mom forced Jimmy and me to hug after we'd fought. I decided to quit while I was ahead. Or rather, quit while I wasn't too far behind.

"*Gregory Scott!*"

What was this? Now Dad was calling me? *Jimmy.* That stinker. He'd gone and told Dad so I'd get two lectures. What if Dad handed out his own punishment?

I found Dad at the kitchen table, staring at a laptop. Jimmy was nowhere to be seen. I stood there for a minute. Dad continued reading the screen.

"What, Dad?"

Dad looked over at me. "Huh? What?"

I thought about saying never mind and leaving, but realization crept over Dad's face. "Greg, what did you do to Jimmy?"

"Mom already told me I had to vacuum."

"You spit carrots at him?"

"Yeah, but—"

Dad smacked his forehead, and I stopped talking.

"Is this going to become a habit?" Dad asked. "You spitting carrots at your brother?"

"No," I grumbled.

"Okay," Dad said. "Did Mom already give you a lecture?"

"Yes."

"What'd she say?"

"She said I shouldn't spit carrots at anybody. Because Jesus never did. And I can't argue with Jesus."

"Your mother is right."

I sighed. "Can I go now? I have to vacuum."

"Yes." Dad looked back to his screen, and I turned to leave.

"Wait, Greg," Dad said, looking over his shoulder. "Why did you spit carrots at Jimmy in the first place? It's not exactly your finest hour."

Finally, I got to tell my side of the story.

"I was eating some carrots, and Jimmy wanted one," I said. "I told him to go get his own. He wouldn't, and then he threw me to the ground, sat on my belly, and tickled my armpits. I had my mouth full of carrots, and when I laughed, they kind of flew out and hit him in the face." Okay, that last part was maybe a stretch. When I realized I was laughing so hard the carrots were going to come out, I intentionally aimed at Jimmy's face. And blew. Maybe that makes me a bad boy, but it seemed like the right thing to do at the time.

Dad stared at me. I wondered if he was going to add to my punishment. Or give me another lecture.

"Let me get this straight," Dad said. "You had your mouth full of carrots, and Jimmy threw you to the ground and tickled you?"

I nodded.

Dad kept staring at me. I couldn't quite read his face.

"Okay," he said. "Listen up. Everything your mother said is right. Your mother's never wrong. You shouldn't spit carrots at Jimmy. But if he's going to tickle you with carrots in your mouth, he's got to expect a few carrots in his face. If he does that again, feel free to spit as many carrots as you want."

I could feel my eyes bug out.

"*Jimmy!*" Dad yelled. "Get the vacuum."

I figured it would be pushing my luck to let Dad see me laugh. I knew when to quit. I raced outside with the sweet taste of carrots and justice on the tip my tongue.

# Conversations in Fatherhood

Father: William, you shouldn't hit your brother. In fact, you shouldn't hit anybody.

10yo: Unless they are trying to kidnap you. My teacher said if somebody is trying to steal you, then you can kick them in the—

Father: Yes, well . . . That is the only time you can hit or kick somebody.

7yo: What if they're trying to kill you?

Father: I don't think you're going to have many problems with people trying to—

5yo: You can hit somebody if they have machetes stuck all over them.

Father: Uh . . .

# CHAPTER 4

*My father has influenced my life in a million ways. He has cared for me.*
*He has passed on skills and traits. I'm sure my sense of humor comes from*
*him. My father also writes stories and poems. It would seem wrong to*
*write a book about Father's Day without including a story and*
*a poem from the man who taught me to love words.*

THE CHILDREN ATTACHED TO THE three noses on the windowpane could
have sworn they smelled the wet snow outside. They had been watching
the snow fall most of the afternoon, thinking about Christmas. Would
Santa come? And if he did, what would he bring? In recent years, Dad had
been away at war, and even though Santa had come, the gifts he'd brought
had been more practical than fun. Their hopes this year—now that Dad
was back *and* had a job—were greater than they had been in years.

From behind them came Dad's voice. "David, run out behind the house
and bring in the old washtub. You know, the one with the hole in it."

Dad had returned home from the navy four months earlier and, because
he had been in the South Pacific, was still tan and dark. His black hair, which
had been cut short to meet naval regulations, was only now beginning to
grow longer than the quarter inch he had worn then. In contrast to his hair
and complexion, his eyes were an icy blue that seemed to twinkle when he
was happy.

David, the oldest at eight, ran to obey his father. Dad rounded up Michael,
who was four, and Cathy, who was five, and took them to the front room by
the Christmas tree.

When David returned with the tub, Dad tousled his sandy hair and
brought out one of Mom's old stockings and a pair of scissors from deep
in his overalls pocket.

"We're going to play a trick on old Santa Claus this year, kids. Do you
want to help me?" he said in a low whisper.

"How are you going to do that, Dad? Does Mom know about this?" Mike asked.

"Is it safe?" Cathy said.

"You can't do that, Dad," David added. "You can't trick Santa. He knows everything."

"No, kids," Dad said. "Santa's getting old and probably hasn't had time to get his eyes checked this year. I bet he's half blind and won't be able to see what we're going to do."

"What are you going to do, Dad?" Mike asked again.

"Well, I'll tell you what. I'm going to hang Mom's old nylon stocking here on the mantel. Underneath that, I'm going to put the old washtub. Then I'm going to cut a hole in the toe of Mom's stocking and let it hang into the tub. When Santa starts to fill my stocking, he won't see the candy falling into the tub. He'll keep trying to fill my stocking until the tub is full."

Without waiting for the children to respond, Dad cut the hole, hung the stocking, and positioned the tub. When he was finished, Mike, who had been the quietest throughout the proceedings, asked, "Dad, if your trick on Santa works, will you share your candy?"

"Sure, I will. In fact, I'll get so much candy that you might as well not even hang your stockings. I'll get so much that if we split it four ways, we'll all get sick."

Mike was surprised by Dad's reply, and the silence that greeted this suggestion was long. Finally, it was determined that the three children would still hang their own stockings—not to be greedy, but so that if Dad's idea worked, they would be able to give the candy in their stockings to Mom and still share with Dad.

Dad agreed.

On Christmas Eve, the family read the traditional scriptures and watched the lights on the tree. The children hoped that by some seasonal magic, Santa really had received their Christmas messages. Eventually, everyone was sent to bed.

It can't be said that David, Cathy, and Mike dreamed of sugarplums. The three of them had never seen one. But they certainly had visions of snow, trees, and gifts. And most assuredly, they dreamed of a tub full of candy. Maybe even the whole corner of the room would be filled with more candy than they had ever seen. Dreams like these are enough to keep a child asleep for a long time.

When the light of morning came, two parents found themselves being watched by three sets of sleepless eyes.

As Mom opened her eyes, the children grew bolder and approached the bed.

"Do we have to eat first?" Cathy asked.

"I want to save room for my candy," Mike said.

"Can we just go in the other room and see?" David asked.

The rush of questions woke Dad. "Come on, kids. Let's go see how much candy we tricked out of old Santa." They retreated to the dining room, and when the folding doors were opened, the sights and smells of Christmas met them.

All eyes turned to the mantel, searching for the mountain of candy in the tub. But rather than being filled to the brim with sweets and goodies, the tub was full of coal. There was a small bit of kindling and a note on top. The children looked at their stockings. Each one was full, bursting with nuts, candies, and fruit. All, that is, except Dad's nylon stocking. It was hanging there empty of any Christmas joy. Dad went over to the tub, picked up the note, and read it out loud.

*Dear Mr. Jensen,*

*What am I to do with you? Trying to play a trick on old Santa. What I have left you is what you deserve. Please try to be a better example to your children.*

*Love, Santa*

Dad wadded up the paper, threw it on the grate, took some kindling from his tub, and started the fire.

None of the children dared say anything. None of them reminded their father that they were going to give their stockings to Mom and share Dad's candy. And, oh, how they were relieved that they had left their stockings up. If Santa was going to do things that way, they were glad it had been done to their dad and not to them.

The fire began to warm the chilly air, and soon the happy sounds of Christmas filled the room.

It was good to have their father home this Christmas. The last two years without him had been quiet and lonely. To have joy and happiness and fun together, as well as treats, was all the Christmas season should be. And even though Dad's trick hadn't worked, it had been fun to dream about.

Through the rest of the day, when no one was looking, each of the children slipped Dad a little of their candy. And through the rest of the day, though no one was looking, Dad would smile and put piece after piece of coal on the fire.

# Conversations in Fatherhood

15yo: I got a 92 on my algebra test.

Father: Good for you! Did you learn from your mistakes?

15yo: Yes.

Father: What did you learn?

15yo: Not to make mistakes.

# CHAPTER 5

*Tea Party Part I*

"Hey, Dad?"

I knew that tone. My daughter always followed those words with a tugging of my arm and looking at me with her two brown eyes under pleading eyebrows.

"Dad, Mr. Cleon wants you to come to our tea party. Please, Dad?"

I'm like any father. I love my little girl. My little Anya. I'd take a bullet for her. It's in the job description, and I'm fine with that. But a tea party? A tea party with stuffed animals?

"Honey," I said. "Daddy's watching the football game. And it's not just any game. It's the BYU-Utah game. Do you know what that means?"

"No." Anya shook her head.

I realized there was no way to explain the significance of this game to my little daughter.

Don't get me wrong. I knew the valiant thing would be to go have a little tea party with my girl. If this were a Hallmark commercial, I'd snap the TV off, wander down the hall, and we'd have fake tea while laughing together in slow motion. Violins would serenade us while some announcer would say something in a deep and rustic voice.

But life didn't really work that way. I could have fake tea with her in another twenty minutes—*after* the game. Or maybe another hour or two . . . after the postgame show. We could bond then just as well as we could bond right now.

"Honey," I said. "I have a better idea. Instead of a tea party, why don't you sit here and watch the football game with me? That could be just as fun, right?"

Anya didn't look convinced. "But Mr. Cleon is waiting. And the tea will get cold."

I thought about playing the Word of Wisdom card and bringing the kibosh down on the whole tea party, but decided that was a low blow.

"If there is one thing I've always admired about Mr. Cleon," I said, "it's that he's a very patient and understanding fellow. I'm sure he'll understand if you put off your tea for a few . . . minutes. To watch the game and bond with your dad."

Anya shook her head. "I don't think you know Mr. Cleon very well."

I pulled my daughter up next to me on the couch. "I'll explain it to him, and we can use the microwave to warm up the tea after the game."

My daughter sat in silence next to me on the couch. She'd never watched football, so I knew she didn't understand what was happening, but she sat patiently nonetheless. A familiar and obnoxious feeling started to creep in and chew with scissorlike teeth at the corners of my heart.

Guilt.

Not a problem. I know how to fend off guilt.

"Sweetheart, would you like me to explain how the game works?"

Anya shrugged her shoulders. "Sure."

There! Let the Hallmark commercial people come and film this. A father teaching his daughter the ins and outs of America's favorite pastime. Let their sappy violins play while I point at the television and Anya laughs at my witty example of unsportsmanlike conduct.

"Okay," I said. "The first and most important thing to remember is that the guys wearing the blue uniforms are the good guys, and the guys wearing the red uniforms are the bad guys. Can you remember that?"

Anya shook her head. "My favorite color is red."

I cleared my throat. "Well . . . you can like red as a color, but we're cheering for the boys in blue. Those are the good guys."

"Why are the red guys bad?" Anya asked. "Didn't they pick up their toys? Or did they spit at their little brother in the bathtub like Peter did yesterday?"

"No," I said. "It's just that the blue guys are always the good guys. Unless they play Utah State. Then it's a little more complicated. That's just how things work."

"I think I like the red guys," Anya said. "Look, they even have more points."

"Hey," I said. "Who taught you how to read the scoreboard?"

"I'm not a baby, Daddy."

"Apparently not," I said. "Just don't feel sad when the blue team scores more points and wins the game."

"How do you score points?" Anya asked.

"Ah," I said. "Excellent question. Right now the blue team has the ball. There are only four minutes left in the game. If they can take the ball all the way to the left—they keep running until there isn't any more grass—then they score a touchdown. Once they do that, they'll get six more points. Then they'll be ahead of the bad guys, and they'll win the game."

"Well, they're not going to score a touchdown if all they do is stand around in a circle."

"They're not standing around," I said. "That's called a 'huddle.' They're planning how to beat the red guys."

"My red team isn't standing in a circle," Anya proclaimed. "It looks like they already know what to do next."

"*Your* red team?" I decided not to press the issue. "Let's just see what happens."

BYU broke the huddle and crouched on the line of scrimmage.

"Ohh, I like that," Anya said. "They're all lined up nice and pretty."

The center snapped the ball, and I felt Anya tense up next to me. She reached over and put her arms around my waist.

"They're fighting!" she cried. "Somebody make them stop. Tell them to stop!"

I hugged my daughter. "They're not fighting," I reassured her. "That is how they play the game. Remember what I told you? The blue team is trying to take the ball to the left. And the red team is trying to stop them."

Anya relaxed. "Oh," she said. "That's good."

By this time, the quarterback had passed the ball, and the play was over.

"Wait," Anya said. "Why did they stop fighting?"

"The play is dead," I said.

Anya's eyes went wide, and she put her hands to her cheek. "Somebody died?"

This was harder than I'd thought.

"No," I reassured her. "Nobody died. The play was declared . . . you see . . . um . . . See those guys in the black-and-white-striped shirts?"

"Uh-huh."

"Whenever they blow their whistles, everybody has to stop fighting."

Anya was quiet for a minute. "Maybe you should get one of those whistles for when Peter fights with me."

"Or when you fight with Peter?" I asked. "I'd even get me one of those shirts if I thought it would work."

"Here they go again," Anya said, pointing at the television. "I think I like it better when they are just lined up and not fighting. Couldn't they just stay lined up?"

"Lining up is nice," I agreed. "But you must push forward if you want to make progress in life. Even when there are things fighting against you."

How was *that*, Hallmark commercial guys? I even threw a life lesson into the mix. I was like a father ninja.

BYU snapped the ball again.

"Somebody blow a whistle!" Anya screamed. "Make them stop!"

The play ended with a quarterback sack. I forget exactly how I expressed my frustration, but Anya recognized that one of the words I'd said was on Mom's we-don't-use-that-word-in-this-house list.

"Oh," she said and covered her mouth with her hands. Through her fingers, she whispered, "Daddy said a naughty."

"That's because the red team was very rude," I said.

"They were?" Anya said. "What'd they do?"

"The captain of our blue team was trying to throw the ball down the field," I explained. "And your red team pushed right through the blue team, grabbed our captain, and threw him to the ground. Isn't that mean? Are you sure you want to cheer for a team that has such rude players?"

"I don't know," Anya said, and she sounded like she was really considering her options. "The blue team seems pretty rude too. All anybody does in this game is line up and fight."

"That's not all they do," I said. "Look, the red team has been so rude, the blue team has decided they are going to kick the ball. See that person all the way back from the line? He's going to kick the ball to the red team. See how nice the blue team is?"

The center snapped the ball.

"Oh!" Anya said. "That's a high kick. I like that. I like that a lot."

"Just one more reason you should cheer for the blue team," I said. "In fact—"

"Oh my goodness, that red guy can run fast!"

I watched in horror as a Ute player broke two tackles and then ran down the sideline.

"Get him!" I yelled at the screen.

"Why is the blue team chasing him?" Anya asked.

"Because he has the ball!"

"But they just gave it to him," Anya said. "If they didn't want him to have the ball, they shouldn't have kicked it to him in the first place. Oh look, he's going to run out of grass!"

I smacked my forehead as the referee threw up his hands to signal a touchdown.

"And now we have even more points!" Anya declared. "A lot more points." She started counting on her fingers.

I clicked the TV off.

"Hey!" Anya protested. "The game was just getting good."

"It was *not* getting good," I said. "It was getting very bad. Besides, I think Mr. Cleon has been waiting long enough."

# Conversations in Fatherhood

Dad: "Did anybody bring the face cards?"

14yo: "Kennan did, but they're all nines."

# CHAPTER 6

## Tea Party Part II

I STOOD UP AND TRIED to put the frustrations of the game behind me. Anybody who says, "It's only a game," doesn't realize the word *fan* is short for *fanatic*.

Anya took my hand and guided me back to her room. When I entered the room, I could tell she'd gone to a great deal of work setting up her tea party. I felt a small twinge of guilt for putting her off.

She'd dragged the piano bench from the living room and dropped two pillow cases over the top to serve as a tablecloth. Four small chairs waited at each side of the bench. Her plastic tea set—with the same pieces I'd often tripped over and stepped on—was set out with care.

A large teddy bear sat in one of the plastic chairs. His wide eyes were a little disconcerting. It was as if his face had been frozen in a moment of sheer terror. I imagined what he might say if he could really speak.

*For the love of all that's holy, don't drink the tea!*

The other three chairs stood empty.

I pushed one of the chairs back and sat on the floor. I didn't want to start the tea party off by crushing a chair. I held a hand out to the teddy bear. "It's a pleasure to meet you, Mr. Cleon," I said.

The bear continued to stare at me in abject horror, like I'd just committed the mother of all faux pas.

"Dad!" Anya exclaimed. She sat in the chair opposite me. "That's not Mr. Cleon. That's Franklin Delano."

I raised my eyebrows. "Oh . . . well, it's a pleasure to meet you, Mr. President." I shook the bear's paw and avoided looking into his wild eyes.

"Daddy," Anya scolded. "Don't be silly. He's not the president."

I decided not to press the issue. "Well?" I asked. "Where is Mr. Cleon? I motioned to the empty chair, leaned forward, and whispered, "Is he invisible?"

Anya smacked her forehead. "Daddy, Mr. Cleon isn't pretend. He's real, just like Franklin Delano."

"Then where is he?" I asked. "I thought you said he was going to have tea with us."

Anya shrugged. "I told you he wasn't very patient. You probably made him mad, and he left. It's not good to make Mr. Cleon mad."

I couldn't help but imagine Franklin Delano speaking up to my left. *She's right. You don't want to upset Mr. Cleon. Bad things happen when Mr. Cleon is angry.*

I've never understood the appeal of a tea party. It didn't seem like there was any point. You pretended to make tea and then pretended to drink it. I needed a purpose, and I saw one in Mr. Cleon.

"Well, I hope I didn't offend him too much," I said. "Luckily, I'm quite the charming guy. I bet by the end of the tea party, Mr. Cleon and I will be best friends."

I looked at the tea set more closely. I could see the order in which Anya had placed the plastic ware. In front of each chair were a teacup, a saucer, and a small plate. In front of Franklin Delano, instead of a small plate, there was a piece of paper that had been cut in a crude circle.

Once again, I imagined what poor Franklin Delano might say if he had a voice. *Will you look at this? I don't even have a plate. I have a piece of paper. What am I supposed to do with a piece of paper?*

I seemed to remember stepping on one of Anya's plates. I'd only cracked it, but I'd tossed it in the trash, hoping she wouldn't notice. I felt justified at the time because she hadn't put her toys away. Now I felt yet another twinge of guilt.

In the center were a teapot and two larger plates. I reached out and picked up the teapot. "May I pour you some tea?" I asked in what I thought was a proper British accent.

Anya reached out and felt the side of the teapot. She tsked her tongue. "Just as I thought," she said. "It's gone cold."

Another twinge of guilt. That was my fault.

*It's gone cold! The tea's gone cold! What are we supposed to do now?*

I wished Franklin Delano would stop yelling in my mind.

"No worries!" I said. "Luckily, you've got a microwave." I pointed to the kitchen set against the wall. "Thirty seconds and we'll be drinking hot tea."

Anya shook her head. "I don't think you should microwave it. Mr. Cleon is a traditionalist. He doesn't like his tea microwaved."

"Nonsense," I said, seeing a chance to educate my daughter and also wondering where she'd learned the word *traditionalist.* "It's a simple matter of physics. Whether you use the heat from a stovetop or microwaves or even the sun, you end up with hot water. It doesn't taste different; you've just used a different source of heat to reach the same conclusion."

I was proud of my little speech, but Anya still looked unconvinced. "You'll have to explain it to Mr. Cleon," she said. "If he even comes back."

I got up and took the teapot over to the kitchen set. I placed the teapot in the microwave, pretended to hit a few buttons, and then waited. Franklin Delano stared in sheer terror from his seat.

*Mr. Cleon is going to be very angry about this.*

Anya sat patiently. I made a beeping sound and opened the door. I reached in and then pulled my hand out quickly. "Oh my!" I said. "That's piping hot. See how that works? You can't argue with the laws of physics."

I carried the teapot over to the table and pretended to pour it in each cup—except Mr. Cleon's. "I'll wait to pour Mr. Cleon's tea," I said, a little proud of the detail of my imagination. "I wouldn't want it to get cold in his teacup."

Anya picked up a plate. "Biscuit?"

"Why, I don't mind if I do."

I pretended to pick up a cookie and place it on the small plate in front of me. Anya took one too and then gave one to Franklin Delano.

*Biscuit! I love me a good biscuit!*

Anya returned the plate to the table and held up the second plate.

"Little hot dog?" she asked. "They have spicy barbecue sauce."

Little hot dogs with barbecue sauce were one of Anya's favorite foods. On her birthday, she'd asked for a cake made out of little hot dogs and barbecue sauce. I made a mental note to pick some up at the store the next time I went. It would be a surprise.

I went to take a little hot dog, and Anya pulled the plate away. "Not with your fingers, Daddy. You'll get sauce all over. Use a toothpick."

"A toothpick?" I didn't see any toothpicks.

"On the other side of the plate," Anya said, motioning with her head.

I moved my hand to the other side of the plate and left it hovering there. I raised my eyebrows in a questioning manner. Anya nodded. I pretended to pick up a toothpick and then speared an imaginary chunk of meat.

"Mmmmm," I said. "I might need another." I made another spearing motion and then placed the invisible food on the plate in front of me.

Anya served Franklin Delano.

*Saucy little hot dog!*

"I do hope I get to meet Mr. Cleon," I said after a couple sips of imaginary tea, "so I can apologize properly for holding up the tea party."

Anya said nothing but continued to eat and drink. After a few moments, she got up and went to her bed. She came back with one of Peter's GI Joe action figures in her hand. The figure had a beard, a sailors' cap, dark blue pants, and a light blue shirt. Anya had also dressed it up with a pink frilly dress.

Anya balanced him on top of the table in Mr. Cleon's spot.

I waited for a proper introduction.

"Oh," Anya said as if she'd just noticed the figure. "Mr. Cleon. It's so nice of you to join us."

"Mr. Cleon," I said, deciding I wouldn't try to shake his little hand for fear of tipping him over. "I've heard a lot about you. I'm very pleased that we finally get to meet."

*Don't make him mad. You'll never make it out of the room alive.*

I picked up the teapot and pretended to pour it in Mr. Cleon's cup.

"He doesn't want any," Anya said. "He said he can smell the microwaves."

I thought about informing Mr. Cleon that he was crazy but remembered my goal. Mr. Cleon and I were to become best of friends.

"I'm so sorry, my dear chap. That's completely my fault. Let me brew you a fresh pot."

I carried the teapot to the sink and went through the motions of dumping out the microwave-tainted tea, filling up the pot with water, and then placing it on the stove.

I returned to the table.

"The tea will be hot in a moment, Mr. Cleon."

Anya served Mr. Cleon some biscuits and a few hot dogs.

"That's a nice dress you've got on, my good man," I said. "I've never seen anybody with a beard pull off that shade of pink."

"Daddy," Anya said. "He's only wearing it because he lost a bet. With Ms. Perkins."

"Oh really?" I asked. "Who is Ms. Perkins? And what was the bet?"

*Ms. Perkins isn't around anymore, if you know what I mean.*

"Ms. Perkins is a ninja," Anya said. "Mr. Cleon bet that she couldn't break through ten planks of wood with her forehead. But she did, so now Mr. Cleon has to wear a dress for a week."

"I see," I said, although I wasn't sure if I did. "And what was Mr. Cleon betting?"

"He was betting what he always bets," Anya said. "He wants to take Ms. Perkins out to Taco Time for chili cheese tots."

Another of Anya's favorite foods.

I broke into a wide grin. "Mr. Cleon! You've taken a liking to ol' Ms. Perkins, eh, buddy?"

I stuck out my elbow and meant to just go through the motions of nudging the little guy, as one friend might do playfully to another, but unfortunately, I didn't pull back in time. My elbow hit Mr. Cleon square in the head, and he went sprawling to the floor.

*Holy honk!*

"I'm sorry!" I said while Anya picked up Mr. Cleon off the floor. "Mr. Cleon, I'm so sorry."

Anya balanced him on the table once again. I waited for my daughter to tell me what Mr. Cleon's reaction was, but she just sipped her tea and stared at me.

*You'll never leave this room alive*, Franklin Delano whispered at my left.

"Uh . . ." I said, making a mental effort not to look over at Franklin Delano. "Oh, Mr. Cleon, sounds like your tea is ready."

I went over to the pretend stove and brought back the teapot. I made a great show of pouring tea into Mr. Cleon's cup. "Would you like some sugar?"

Anya set down her teacup. "Mr. Cleon says he can get his own sugar, thank you very much."

I cleared my throat. Mr. Cleon was proving to be a hard nut to crack. "So uh . . . Is Ms. Perkins pretty?"

Anya nodded. "She's very pretty. But unfortunately, it will never work out."

"What won't work out?" I asked.

"She will never date Mr. Cleon."

"Why not?"

Anya looked at me with sad eyes. "She's a pacifist."

"She's a . . ." I didn't mean to insult my girl's intelligence, but I had to ask. "Do you know what that means?"

Anya nodded. "It means she doesn't like to fight."

"So she's a ninja pacifist?" I asked.

"Yep."

"And Mr. Cleon?"

"He's in the navy."

"I see."

I took a sip of my pretend tea and looked over at Mr. Cleon in a dress. "Well, just because he's in the navy doesn't necessarily mean he likes violence."

"He's also a pirate," Anya said. "In his spare time. Usually on the weekends."

"A pirate."

Anya nodded.

"Well . . . I can understand how that might cause a problem with Ms. Perkins. She being a pacifist and all."

I had a new plan. If I could get Mr. Cleon and Ms. Perkins together . . . Mr. Cleon would be forever in my debt. He'd love me. Together, we could terrorize poor Franklin Delano until he tipped right out of his chair.

Anya looked at her wrist. I noticed she'd drawn a watch on her arm with a ballpoint pen. "Tea time is over. Thank you, Dad." She stood up.

"Wait," I said. "The tea party was just getting good." I felt silly. I'd always grumbled about the state of my daughter's room. Stuffed animals everywhere. Toys dressed up in the wrong clothes. I'd assumed she just didn't care, but . . . she was living in an entirely different world in here. And I wanted to learn more.

"Wouldn't you like another cup of tea?" I asked. "Or hot dogs. I could go get some real hot dogs."

Anya shook her head. "I'm going to go over to Alice's house."

I looked back to the table. Franklin Delano sat there, terrified. Mr. Cleon had tipped forward, his head dunked into his teacup as if he were drowning his sorrows.

I looked back at Anya. "Well then," I said. "Can I at least come back tomorrow?"

Anya walked over and kissed me on the cheek. "I'll have to check with Mr. Cleon."

# Conversations in Fatherhood

Lawn mower—$499.99 + tax

Blade Sharpened—$29.00 + tax

Gasoline—$3.89 + tax

Watching your son mow the lawn for the first time, hit a metal pipe, and ruin the entire setup? ($499.99 + 29.00 + $3.89) X 2

For all the things money can buy, there is cold hard cash. For learning life lessons, there is even more cold hard cash. Cold hard cash and a lot of tongue biting.

# CHAPTER 7

KING OF THE WORLD

If I were the King of this world
or His Son,
of all my creations
t'would be hardest to watch
the death of faith in
a child not yet grown.

The death seen in the eyes
when a friend is untrue,
when the child has been used
and then laughed at too.

To watch him turn to hide a tear
afraid that "weakness" will draw wrath near
at a time when the heart is so close to bursting
yet the soul of the child
is so awfully thirsting
for love and can find no shelter near.

T'wer I the King, I could not hear
that soul cry out.

# Conversations in Fatherhood

Dad: "I saw your Christmas list."

10yo: "Oh yeah?"

Dad: "Yeah. I saw the first thing on your list was a fake eye."

10yo: "Yep."

Dad: "Uh . . . Why do you want a fake eye?"

10yo: "So I can scrunch it into my eye, and when somebody pats me on the back, I'll drop it on the floor."

Dad: "Oh. Of course."

# CHAPTER 8

"What about you, Isaac? What is your favorite Christmas memory?"

The room was dim and filled with color. The Christmas tree lights were the only source of light. Outside, the snow was piled deep, but inside, the room was warm with Christmas spirit.

My children sat on the couch, huddled under blankets. You could tell it was Christmas Eve because two of them were sharing the same blanket without fighting. It was late, but their eyes sparkled as only children's eyes can on the night before Christmas.

"I liked when we got the dinosaur stuffed animals!" Isaac said. "Santa Claus brought so much stuff it filled the table."

"Okay," I said. "That's everybody. Let's get to bed so Santa can come."

"That's not everybody," Spencer said. "What about you and Mom?"

"I think somebody just doesn't want to go to bed," I said.

The kids insisted, and my wife shared a memory of Christmas from her childhood. Then it was my turn.

"Well, I don't know if I should tell you my favorite memory," I said. "I don't think you'll like it." That, of course, made them want to hear it even more. I liked to think I was a pretty good storyteller, and in a moment, I had them begging me to tell them my story.

"Well," I said. "Three years ago, Spencer was old enough to read a clock. Not just read the clock but understand what it meant too."

"I'm kind of bright that way," Spencer said, grinning.

"So Mom and I had told Spencer he couldn't wake up anybody until 6:00 in the morning. That's pretty early."

"Can't we get up at 5:55 tomorrow?" John said. "Please?"

My kids and I had been over this at least a dozen times over the past week. We'd haggled like two old men at a farmers' market. They'd started at 3:00 a.m. I'd started at noon. We'd ended up at the same time we'd ended up every year. 6:00. Not a minute sooner.

"It's 6:00," I said with a grin. "We already agreed."

The boys were too excited to argue.

"Actually, that's part of the story," I said. "You see, I really don't like waking up in the morning. I like sleeping in. I don't get many days off of work, and Christmas is one of them. The only problem?"

I paused and watched five sets of eyes stare at me.

"The only problem," I continued, "is that you boys like to get up early so you can open presents."

Five heads bobbed up and down.

"So what is a father to do?" I asked. "Actually, it turned out to be quite simple. Three years ago, I went into Spencer's room and moved the clock backward two hours. So when Spencer woke up in the middle of the night, he thought it was two hours earlier and he went back to sleep. When he finally woke up and saw his clock read 6:00, it was actually 8:00. I got to sleep in, and you boys didn't realize a thing. Isn't that smart?"

Disbelief. Astonishment. Horror. There was stunned silence for about three seconds, and then everybody was yelling at once.

"You cheater!"

"You didn't do that. You're lying!"

"I'm going to get you!"

I couldn't help but laugh. "I've done it every year since then."

Spencer, the oldest, smacked his forehead. "That's why Grandma and Grandpa Buckley came over so early last year. Because it wasn't early."

I grinned and nodded. "Yep. I always set the clocks back to the right time sometime in the morning. You kids are having so much fun, you just figure that time is flying by."

"But that's like robbing us of two hours on Christmas Day!" John was almost screaming. "Dad's a robber!"

"Well," I said, "I don't know if I'd go that far. But the gig is up. I certainly couldn't pull it off again this year, now that you know about it."

There was more good-natured grumbling and teasing, and then we said prayers and got everybody tucked into bed. All five boys had their sleeping bags set up in Spencer's room so they could get up at the same time.

"Remember," I said. "6:00. No earlier."

"I think we should get up at 2:00," Spencer said. "Since you've stolen time from us the last three Christmases."

"Good night," I said and then closed the door. I stood in the hall for a moment and listened to five boys talking excitedly about the next morning.

"Dad is not going to trick us this year," John said. "I'm setting my watch."

"Come here, guys," I heard Spencer say. "I have a plan."

Whatever the plan was, I didn't hear it. The boys spoke in hushed whispers, and I heard muffled laughter. After a time, I went out to the living room and read.

My wife and I put out the presents we had for our kids before turning in.

"Are you going to set the clocks back this year?" she asked.

"I don't know," I said. "Now that the boys know, it would be much harder to fool them."

"I noticed you didn't say no," my wife said.

"You're right," I said, grinning in the darkness. "I didn't."

\* \* \*

"Dad! It's time to get up!"

It was a physical impossibility to fall back to sleep when five sets of eyes stared at me and five sets of fingers poked me in the ribs.

I looked at the clock. 6:00. I rubbed my eyes. "Hey!" I said. "How did you . . . I set your clocks back. I even got your watches."

It was true. I'd set their clocks back, as well as four watches—Isaac, the youngest, didn't have one.

"We put John's alarm clock from downstairs under the bed!" Spencer was beside himself. "You changed all of them except for that one."

The boys were howling with laughter now. I told them to get out so I could get dressed, and then we'd start Christmas.

We forced the kids to eat a bowl of cold cereal. I wanted them to have something at least halfway healthy before they started eating chocolate and candy orange slices. Breakfast was over in sixty seconds, and we started the traditions of Christmas.

One by one, each family member took a turn opening one of their presents. Everybody else would *ooh* and *ahh* over it, and then we'd move on to another present. After a short time, all of the presents were gone and we were lost in a sea of wrapping paper, plastic wrap, and empty boxes. The chaos of Christmas was in full swing.

My wife sat next to me, and we watched our five happy boys exploring their new treasures.

"You shouldn't have told them," my wife said.

"Told them what?" I asked.

"About the clocks," she said. "If you hadn't told them, you could have done it another year."

"But there was no challenge to it," I said. "It's not as fun when there isn't a challenge. And besides, sometimes doing something isn't enough. You want other people to see what you've done."

"Are you going to try again next year?"

"Of course," I said. "I'm going for five years in a row."

"Five years . . . but you didn't do it this year."

I smiled.

My wife sat up and looked at her watch then looked over at me, her eyes wide. "How did you . . ."

I tried looking modest but more than likely failed miserably. "I set their main alarm clock and all of their watches back four hours. Then I found the alarm under the bed—"

"How did you know they'd hidden it under the bed?"

"We have eight timepieces in our house that have an alarm. It's a simple matter of finding them all and accounting for each one. I noticed John's clock wasn't in his room, so I looked for it in the bedroom. It wasn't hard to find. They had to plug it in. So I set that clock back two hours," I continued. "And then I set the clock in our room back two hours, along with the rest of the clocks in the kitchen and living room. The boys woke up. Half the clocks tell them it was four in the morning, but the clocks they don't think I've found tell them it's six. It's really eight. They think they've outsmarted me."

My wife stared at me with a look I thought said, *You're crazy, you realize that?* But in my mind, I pretended it was admiration. "So are you going to tell them?" she asked.

"Not right away," I said. "That would be rude."

Later, over Christmas dinner, after the clocks had been returned to their proper time, the boys began to tease me.

"You can't trick us, Dad," Jared said. "Next year we're going to get up even earlier!"

I looked at my wife and smiled. "You're right," I said. "I learned an important lesson today. You have to wake up pretty early to fool my boys."

The boys continued eating, but I noticed my oldest son looked at his watch and then back at me. The glint in his eye made him look like Clint Eastwood.

He suspected. Three hundred and sixty-five days until next Christmas, and already, the game was afoot.

## Conversations in Fatherhood

Dad: "Good night, sweet pea."

5yo: "Good night, sweet poop."

Dad: "What?"

5yo: "You said sweet pee, so I said sweet poop."

# CHAPTER 9

"SON OF A—"

"Sweetheart!" I left the kitchen and stepped into the living room. "You remember the kids are in the house, right? How is the game going?"

My wife sat in the recliner—well, that's not true. My wife never really actually sat down when she watched a football game. She either crouched on the edge of the chair, paced in front of the couch yelling at the television, or lay prostrate on the floor when something really good—or really bad—happened.

"The game," my wife said, biting the word *game* and making it clear to me that any person with half a brain knew this was much more than just a *game*. "The game is going just fine. We're up by ten. What is *not* going fine is this stupid TV."

I stepped farther into the room and looked at the television.

"What are you talking about, honey?" I kept my voice unassuming and calm. I didn't want to come right out and disagree with anything my wife said when she was watching a game. "The picture looks very sharp. The colors are nice and . . . colorful."

My wife gave me a look, and I decided it was better to stop talking.

"It's that tree!" she declared in the same tone that Hercule Poirot would use to accuse the butler of committing a murder. "It's the tree that *you* planted too close to the house."

My wife had picked out and planted that tree herself. She'd picked out and insisted on that spot. I was smart enough to know not to bring that up right now. Possibly ever again.

"I don't understand," I said.

"The wind," she said. "The wind blows the tree branch in front of the satellite, and then I lose the picture. And it *always* happens right at the most important part of the game."

I thought about trying to make a joke. I could laugh and tell her that there could only be one *most* important part of the game, and therefore, the picture would only cut out once.

But that would be like smoking a cigar while pumping gas in the middle of a fireworks factory.

My wife glared at the television, and I took comfort in knowing that her wrath was focused on something else.

I should mention my wife is almost never angry. She loves me. She loves our kids. She's one of the nicest, more caring, helpful, wonderful, thoughtful people I know. She just gets a little . . . passionate when it comes to sports. Actually, that's not entirely true. It's not any sports. It's not even some sports. It's just BYU sports. BYU football in particular.

"There!" she yelled, pointing at the television. "Look! *Look at that!*"

She spoke in the same tone one might use when pointing out to a friend that a cement truck is barreling down the driveway toward the front porch of a house where the couple is sitting and sipping lemonade.

I turned to look at the TV. Sure enough, the picture was a little fuzzy. Maybe.

"Oh my goodness," I said. "That's awful."

I tried to sound sincere. I really did. But I've never been an actor, and my wife knows me too well.

"Don't patronize me, buster," she said through gritted teeth. "It's almost halftime. Get me a rope."

A rope. Wasn't there a scripture that said something like, *Tis better to obey than to try to use logic?* "Yes, dear."

I turned off the burner and removed the pan where I was halfway through making Alfredo. I went to the garage and found some rope. I took it back into the living room and set it on the coffee table. My wife didn't even look at me, her eyes remaining locked on the screen.

I returned to the kitchen and my Alfredo. I'd timed it just right. The meal was ready at halftime. I called in the kids and dished everybody up. My wife came in a few minutes later. The previous Mrs. Hyde was nowhere to be seen.

"Thank you, dear," she said sweetly. "This is delicious. And thank you for the rope. I tied the branch back, and it appears to have fixed the problem."

"I'm very glad to hear that," I said. This time, I *was* sincere.

Everybody ate, and I cleared the table and cleaned the kitchen. My wife returned to the game, and the kids went upstairs to play. I went outside to get the mail. Four steps out the front door, I stopped dead in my tracks. I turned to my right and looked at the tree—the tree that had been planted too close to the house by somebody who will remain nameless.

We'd bought the house four years earlier. The tree had only been six feet at the time we'd planted it. Now it was maybe ten feet. The trunk was only as thick as my forearm, but it was healthy and growing, straight as an arrow into the sky.

Except that right then, it wasn't. It was bent over like a catapult straining to throw its payload into a castle.

My wife had thrown the rope into the top of the tree and then pulled it down and tied it to my oldest son's bike.

"Hey, Hal," my neighbor called from next door. "That's a nice tree you've got there."

"Thanks, Herman." I waved but didn't stop to talk. Herman is an old guy who likes to make me feel small.

I got the mail and went back into the house. My wife was in her pacing mode. That meant things weren't going as well as they had been before halftime. I walked through the living room into the kitchen. I opened my laptop and set about writing.

The next time I looked up at the clock, ninety minutes had passed. That had to put us well into the fourth quarter. I'd heard some noises from the living room, but I couldn't tell if it was cheering or yelling. BYU must have been ahead though, because the substitute cursing hadn't started yet.

"Confound it!" My wife yelled from the living room. "Sons of dishes!"

Maybe I'd spoken too soon.

"*Stupid tree!*"

I looked out the window and saw my oldest son riding his bike down the street. That wasn't good.

I saved my file, closed the laptop, and walked boldly into the lion's den.

It was empty. I looked at the television. The picture looked a little fuzzy.

"Honey?" I called out. My voice sounded small in the suddenly still house. "Honey? How is the game going?"

I heard a *thwack*. It was clear and piercing, and I knew exactly what it was as soon as I heard it.

I raced out the front door. There was my wife with a hatchet in her hand, attacking the tree in our front yard.

"Hey, Hal," Herman called over the fence. "That's a nice wife you've got there."

Two hours earlier, I hadn't dared confront my wife in the living room when she'd had a pillow in her hands. I certainly wasn't going to confront her now that she wielded a hatchet. I sauntered over to Herman.

"She is a pretty nice wife," I said.

I saw the question in Herman's eyes, but I didn't say anything else.

His curiosity finally got the best of him. "What's your wife doing with the hatchet?" he asked.

"She's chopping down a tree," I said.

Herman glared at me. "I can see that. *Why* is she chopping down the tree?"

"It's too close to the house," I said. "I've been meaning to get to it all summer, and instead of complaining that I haven't done it, she's gone ahead and done my job for me."

Herman seemed satisfied with the answer. I watched as my wife hacked at the tree until it slowly started to bend. She dropped the axe and threw herself at the tree. The tree tipped and tipped and then fell to the ground with a crack.

My wife spun on her heels and returned inside.

"Isn't she going to haul the tree off?" Herman asked. "Or dig up the stump?"

"Well," I said. "You can't expect her to do all my work, can you?"

Herman shook his head. "You're a nut, Hal."

"Every family needs one," I said with a smile. "It makes life interesting."

## Conversation in Fatherhood

5yo: Uncle Mike, I have the funniest knock-knock joke in the world.

Uncle Mike: Oh yeah?

5yo: Yeah, you start.

Uncle Mike: Okay. Knock knock.

5yo: *giggling* Who's there?

Uncle Mike: Interrupting cow

5yo: Inter . . . Wait, no, you're not supposed to—

Uncle Mike: MOOOOOOO!

# CHAPTER 10

ONE NIGHT A WEEK.

One night a week and every other weekend.

It never feels like enough.

"Three tickets for *Batman*, please. For the 6:35 showing." My two boys stand behind me. Carl has his Batman shirt on. Luke's just excited to be here. The show is rated PG-13, after all, and he's only twelve.

"Okay, your total is $34.50."

I double-check the board. It's Tuesday night. Discount night. I'm a cheap man—I'd planned this event specifically for tonight because I could save six dollars on tickets. "No, I'm sorry. I said three tickets. I only want three."

The clerk in front of me, a young girl who probably has to go to school early tomorrow, gives me a patient smile. "Yes, sir. The 6:35 showing of *Batman* is in XD. Tickets for our XD screenings are $11.50 each."

I'm sure I look lost. "XD? What is *XD*? I've never heard of that. Did you just make that up?" I smile to show her I'm joking.

"XD," the clerk says. It sounds like she's talking to a five year old. "That stands for extreme definition."

Carl speaks up from behind me. "Wouldn't that be *ED* and not *XD*?"

Carl. He's going to be a lawyer someday. Or an editor.

"Is that like 3D?" I ask.

"Kind of. No. Not really," comes the reply. "We play it on a bigger screen. Plus, we crank up the sound. You know . . . to be extreme."

I look behind me where a line has formed. I lean forward and lower my voice. I don't mind being cheap, but I don't exactly like appearing cheap. "Look, I thought tonight was discount night."

"Oh, it is," the clerk says, smiling again. "You can go to our 7:30 showing. It's only $6.50 per seat."

"That must be RD," Luke says. "Regular definition."

"Or maybe OD," Carl says. "Ordinary definition."

A fifteen-dollar difference. It would be silly to stand around the theater for an entire hour just to save fifteen dollars. I should pay the extra so my boys and I can be extreme.

I stick my credit card back in my wallet. "We'll be back," I say.

"Aren't we going to watch the movie?" Luke sounded worried. "I knew this was too good to be true. Now I'm going to have to wait for my birthday."

"You're not going to have to wait for your birthday," I say. "Just for another hour. I'm old. If I watch a movie in extreme definition, it'll rattle my dentures. We'll catch the next showing."

My boys don't argue. I'm paying for the movie, so they have to play along.

On the bright side, this gives us more time to talk. The movie will be fun, but we won't get to interact once it starts.

"Do you want to go to Tilly's?" Carl asks. "That's where I got my hat."

Carl loves his hat. It has a tail.

"Sure," I say. We walk across the parking lot and poke around in Tilly's for a while. They have T-shirts with logos I don't understand. It makes me feel old.

"Hey, Dad," Luke says. "Do you need a talking mustache?"

Luke is holding a keychain with a plastic mustache. He presses a button, and the mustache says, "Hello there."

"Wonderful," I say. "This store frightens me. Let's go get some Fat Boys."

Six minutes later, we're sitting on a bench, chewing our way through some Fat Boy ice cream sandwiches.

"What time is it?" Luke asks.

I look at my watch. "It's 6:40. We've still got a while."

A family approaches. Four kids. The oldest is a girl who looks to be about Carl's age.

"Hey, Carl," I say under my breath. "Let's see your moves. The girl that's walking this way. Let's see what you got."

"Dad!" I can tell by his voice he's mortified. "Don't say another word."

The family walks by. My oldest son sits there, rigid. Luke giggles the entire time. After the family passes, Carl lets out a sigh of relief.

I cluck my tongue. "I hate to tell you this, Carl, but that was pathetic. On a scale of one to ten, you get a zero. You just sat there."

Carl punches my arm. Luke laughs.

"I'm your father," I say in mock seriousness. "I have to teach you these very important skills. I have to teach you how to make moves on the ladies."

"Holy cow, Dad," Carl says, slapping himself on the forehead. "You're embarrassing yourself."

"I think I'm embarrassing you," I say. "Come on; let's role-play. I'll be the girl. You show me your moves."

Carl rolls his eyes and doesn't even bother replying.

"Well then." I get up and start walking. "We'll just have to do it for real." Luke gets up because he loves to see Carl be embarrassed. Carl follows because there isn't anything else he can do.

We head into Ross. We walk through the pants section then browse the shirts.

"Heads up," I say. "There's a very nice-looking girl at nine o'clock. Show me your moves."

Carl hits me again, grinning but also looking terrified. Luke maintains a constant flow of giggling. The girl passes. Once she's out of earshot, I shake my head.

"Another zero," I say. "It's a good thing I've realized you have a serious deficiency in the moves department. You're in desperate need of some coaching."

"Dad!"

I'm having far too much fun to stop. I suspect he is too. Luke clearly is.

"We need to work out a code phrase," I say. "I can't just say, 'Make your moves,' because the girls might overhear." I think for a moment. "Okay, the code is *Confederate army*. That means you have to show me your moves."

"What?" Carl asks. "Why *Confederate army*?"

"That way if they overhear us, they'll think we're having an in-depth historical discussion. They'll think you're smart, and they'll be more receptive to your moves. And heaven knows, you need all the help you can get."

Another punch to the arm.

We move out of Ross and back toward the movie theater.

"Confederate army," Luke says.

"Uh . . . Those are college students, Luke," I say. "Better leave the spotting to me."

There are more crowds around the theater. Plenty of opportunities. "Confederate army," I say, spotting several girls walking toward us. "Carl, don't let me down!"

Luke's giggling is now completely out of control.

"I can't do anything with Luke making all that noise."

And then it happens. Something beautiful. Carl puts an emphasis on the word *noise* and says it louder than the rest of his sentence. His voice cracks. The girls walk past us. When they are safely out of our bubble, I burst out laughing.

"*That* was your move?" I ask. "To crow like a pterodactyl?"

Now Luke is bent over, holding his belly and laughing hard. I laugh harder, and Carl hits me again.

"Hello," I say. "My name's Carl. Look at what I can do. *Packaw!*" I do my best to sound like a pterodactyl.

"You guys are embarrassing," Carl says, but the grin on his face tells me he's loving the attention.

"Well," I say. "At least you get points for trying. If you just sit there, you're going to get a zero. But the pterodactyl impression gives you a . . ." I pause. "At least a zero point two. It's not much because dinosaur impressions aren't going to score you many points with the ladies, but at least it won't be hard to improve. The good news is, now that we've identified the problem, we can fix it."

We walk in and buy tickets. Carl is laughing. Luke is doing pterodactyl impressions. All three of us probably look like idiots, but we're having the time of our lives.

One night a week.

One night a week and every other weekend.

It's not enough. But the bruises on my arm show that I'm making the most of it.

# Conversations in Fatherhood

14yo: Hey! Have I taught you my new game?

Dad: No. What is it?

14yo: Rock, paper, scissors, lizard, Spock, llama, zombie.

Dad: Oh . . . that sounds . . . complicated.

12yo: What is it? What's the game?

14yo: Rock, paper, scissors, lizard, Spock, Canada, llama, zombie.

Dad: Didn't you just add one?

14yo: Yeah. Sometimes that happens.

Dad: I see. So how does one play this game?

14yo: Currently . . . I have no idea.

# CHAPTER 11

"What'cha doing, Dad?"

"Making breakfast." I'd tried pulling out the pans and pots quietly, but it didn't take much to wake up Jacob.

"Why are you making breakfast?" Jacob asked, his sleepy eyes going wide. "Did somebody steal Mom?"

"Of course not. Don't you remember what day it is?"

Jacob shook his head.

"Mother's Day," I said. "Remember, you colored Mom the nice card yesterday?"

"Oh yeah!" Jacob turned and ran from the room.

"Don't take it to her yet," I called after him. "She's still asleep."

I put two pans on the stovetop and opened the fridge. The groceries I bought last night were all in a bag at the back. I hadn't wanted my wife to see what was on the menu.

Jacob came padding back into the room, a folded paper clutched in his hand.

"We'll put that on the breakfast tray. Does that sound good?" I asked.

Jacob nodded and climbed onto a bar stool.

"Can I crack an egg?" Jacob asked.

I pulled out a bowl and passed it over to Jacob, along with an egg. Jacob was old enough to want to help but not old enough to actually *be* a help. He was also old enough to keep asking until I let him do something. The price of one egg would be worth keeping him occupied.

Jacob cracked the egg on the side of the bowl. "Dang it!" he said. "I kind of got egg shell all over the place."

"That's okay," I said. "Just pick it out." I went to a cupboard. "But you don't want to get your fingers eggy. Here, use a toothpick."

A toothpick wouldn't make it easier . . . In fact, it would probably make it more difficult. But it would keep Jacob occupied for at least twenty minutes.

I chopped onions, green peppers, and mushrooms. Then I pulled potatoes out of the pantry and washed and cubed them while Jacob poked at the eggs. He was making a mess, but the mess was on his side of the counter and not mine, so everything was good.

"Is that for dinner?" Jacob asked. "I hate onions."

"Nope, this is for breakfast," I said. "I'm making scrambled eggs and hash browns."

Jacob stopped poking the eggs and looked at me like I'd just announced Godzilla lived in the washing machine.

"Dad . . ." Jacob was old enough that he'd become aware of other people's feelings. He didn't want to come right out and call me crazy, even if that was exactly what he thought. "You don't put . . . *things* in scrambled eggs. Just eggs."

"Oh?" I said. "And how many times have you cooked eggs?"

"I help Mom all the time," Jacob said, his voice proud. "Mom doesn't put anything in eggs. Except for eggs."

"Well," I said. "Have you ever thought that maybe Mom has been doing it wrong? That maybe this is the right way?"

"Dad!" Jacob didn't even bother replying to that one. I noticed he'd put the toothpick down. He watched me like an owl eying a field mouse.

I turned on the burners and waited for the pans to heat up. I sprinkled water in them and watched the drops scatter and dance across the surface. I dropped butter in both of them and then dumped the onions, peppers, and mushrooms in one and the potatoes in the other.

"What are you doing now?" Jacob asked.

"Making the hash browns." I replied.

Jacob's voice was filled with regret. "You're doing the hash browns wrong, too."

I kept my back to him so I could smile without him seeing. "Am I?" I said. "How am I doing the hash browns wrong?"

"Hash browns come from a bag," Jacob said. "A bag in the freezer. Not from raw potatoes."

"Ah, I see," I said, stirring the food. "Then these aren't hash browns. These are spiced and fried potatoes."

"Oh," Jacob said.

I continued to cook. I prepared a tray with a cream-cheese danish, a cup of fruit, and a glass of juice. I beat some eggs and poured them in the pan with the peppers, mushrooms, and onions. Jacob watched the entire process with a vigilant eye. At several points, he clucked his tongue and shook his head.

Once the eggs were fluffy, I sprinkled on some cheese and covered the pan with the lid. I turned to Jacob. "Would you like to try some?"

Jacob made a face. "Yuck. No. Onions."

I turned off the stove and dished up some eggs and potatoes. I placed the plate on the tray, and Jacob arranged his card between the glass of juice and the plate. We carried the breakfast up to my wife.

"Thank you!" she said. "Oh my, this looks wonderful."

My wife read the card and hugged Jacob. With the glass of juice sitting on the tray, I didn't want Jacob bouncing around the bed.

"Come on, buddy," I said. "Let's get you some breakfast."

Downstairs, I got a plate and dished up some hash browns and eggs. I placed it on the table before Jacob. He shook his head.

"You have to at least try it," I said. "You know the rules."

"I hate onions," Jacob said.

"You can pick them out," I replied.

I dished up my own plate and began to eat. Jacob pushed the food around on his plate. I realized he was separating the mushrooms, peppers, and onions from the rest of his eggs.

"Jacob," I said. "I wouldn't put anything in the eggs that didn't make it taste better. Trust me; try them."

Jacob had finally freed one piece of egg from anything that appeared to be a non-egg. He speared the yellow fluffy mass with his fork and put it hesitantly in his mouth. He chewed. His eyes lit up.

"That's really good!" he said.

"What did I tell you? Dad knows how to cook."

Jacob began to separate more of his egg from the vegetables. "You make really good eggs, Daddy. Next time, you should leave out all the other stuff so I can eat it faster."

"But it's that other stuff that makes it taste so good," I said.

Jacob ignored me. He continued to free his eggs from the "other stuff."

When we were finished, I carried both plates over to the sink. My wife came in, carrying her empty tray.

"Mom," Jacob said. "Dad makes pretty good eggs, doesn't he?"

"He sure does," my wife said. "He makes the best eggs."

I took the tray from my wife and then turned back to Jacob. "Now if we can just get you to eat with a little more boldness, we'll be set," I said. "I don't know where you get your pickiness from."

I went to place the tray in the sink and stopped. I stared at my wife's plate. She'd eaten everything. Eggs, hash browns, danish. Everything except for the green peppers. And the onions. And the mushrooms.

"The eggs really were good," my wife said behind me. "I don't know how you do it."

## Conversations in Fatherhood

Dad: "Another birthday card. Oh, this is very nice! Did you draw it yourself? Is that a birthday cake?"

3yo: "No, that's a monster eating a kid's arm off. But it doesn't go down to his stomach; it goes up to his brain. Ha ha!"

Dad: "Oh yeah . . . Now I see it."

# CHAPTER 12

Letterman was in rare form.

His jokes stumbled into the darkness of our living room. I wrapped my grandmother's afghan tighter around my shoulders. Outside, the wind howled, and if you listened closely enough, you could hear the snow hitting the side of the house.

*Don't go far. We'll be right back after the break.*

One of the benefits of being eighteen was I no longer had a bedtime. When Mom or Dad would suggest I turn in for the night, I'd say something like, "In two more months, I'll be on my mission. And you'll miss me. And you'll wish you could lie in bed and hear me listening to the TV out in the living room instead of just total silence. Total, lonely silence."

I also used this line of reasoning to get ice cream every once in a while. Ice cream *and* Letterman. I was living high on the hog.

Maybe the words *lonely silence* were taking it a bit too far. With eight brothers and a single sister in the house—all younger—I don't think you could call the silence lonely. Maybe *blessed silence* was a better phrase. *Blessed and rare.*

I heard the hall creak. Dad stepped into the living room. He'd come out earlier dressed in his robe, but now he had on Levis and a shirt. In an instant, I knew why. My heart skipped a beat.

"It looks like it's time," Dad said. His voice was calm.

"For the baby?" I asked. "Mom's going to have the baby?"

Dad nodded. "Yep."

"How can you be sure?" I asked the question with a healthy dose of hesitancy. I didn't want details. I knew all about the birds and the bees. More than I wanted to know, in fact. But still, I was curious. I'd heard stories of parents going to the hospital three times in as many days, only to be sent home and told it was false labor.

"After ten children, I've learned not to question," Dad said.

I thought about that. Dad had a point. Mom had been through this ten times. If Mom said the baby was on the way, Dad was probably smart to listen to her.

Dad slipped on his shoes and opened the door.

"Uh, Dad," I said. "Aren't you forgetting somebody important?"

Dad smiled. "I'm just going to start the car so it's nice and warm for Mom."

Dad went outside. I almost returned to my chair and then went to the window instead. I pulled the blind to the side and watched as my father walked to the car. It had been snowing all evening, and there was at least four inches on the sidewalk. Dad climbed inside and started the car. The wipers jerked to life and sent a skiff of snow swirling into the wind. The headlights came on, and I saw snow tumbling through the light.

Getting out of the car, Dad went to the side of the house. He came back with the snow shovel. For a moment, I thought about putting my shoes on and going out to help. But the walk was short, and it felt like this was something Dad wanted to do. His way of serving Mom.

Shoveling didn't take long. He finished and went to the side of the house again. A moment later, he came back with an ice cream bucket filled with rock salt. He threw out handfuls of salt on the dark sidewalk then came back to the door.

I returned to my chair and was under the blanket when Dad walked through. For some reason, I didn't want him to know I'd been watching him. He'd warmed up the car and cleared the walk for Mom. I felt like an uninvited observer of an intimate moment.

*The Top Ten is next; don't go anywhere!*

Dad passed through with a suitcase and a pair of slippers. I heard the wind howl as the door opened and then heard the screen door slam shut.

Dad was calm. A couple of weeks ago, I watched the *I Love Lucy* episode where Lucy has her baby. Of course, all sorts of wild things happened. Ricky was all over the place, Lucy was all over the place. It was a well-worn joke. First-time parents freak out when the baby comes. The dad leaves the mom behind, they forget the suitcase, they run around like chickens with their heads cut off. But my parents looked like they had everything under control.

Mom came into the living room.

I jumped to my feet. "Are you feeling okay?" I asked. "Do you need anything?"

Mom smiled, though I could see pain behind her eyes. "I just need to get to the hospital," she said. "You remember everything we talked about?"

I nodded. "I've got it all planned out," I said. "I'll get the kids fed and on the bus. I can watch Joe and Ellen. Don't worry about a thing."

"I won't," Mom said. "Grandma will be over in the afternoon. And you can call the home teachers if you need anything."

"We'll be fine."

Dad came back to the door and helped Mom into her coat. Another gust of wind and my parents were gone. When they returned, they'd have a new little baby. I'd have a new little brother.

The commercials were almost over. I settled back into the chair and wrapped the blanket around me.

The door opened.

"Almost forgot the baby clothes," Dad said. "We'd have had to bring the little guy back buck naked."

I smiled, and Dad walked past me. David Letterman once again filled the screen.

*Okay, tonight's Top Ten list, brought to you by rabid llamas. That's right. Llamas that have gone rabid are our sponsors for tonight's Top Ten list.*

Laughter from the audience. Dave started at number ten and worked his way toward number one. On number six, I heard a horn honk.

I got out of my chair and walked to the window. Pulling aside the blind, I peeked outside. Mom was in the car. It looked warm. Dad was nowhere to be seen. He had come in for the baby clothes, and I thought he'd gone out, but maybe he hadn't. I turned back to the room.

Dad was standing behind my chair, watching the television. Smiling at Letterman.

The car horn honked again.

"Uh . . . Dad?"

Dad raised his eyebrows, but his eyes never left the screen. "Yes?"

"I think Mom's ready to go. I think she's *really* ready to go."

As if to prove my point, another honk—this one long and loud.

"Letterman's almost done," Dad said. "He's on number three."

"But, Dad . . ."

Another laugh.

I realized I was looking at a man who had been through this ten times as well. Ten pregnancies. Ten labors. Ten deliveries. If Dad felt like he had time for three more jokes, then maybe he was right.

Letterman finished, and my Dad turned to leave. With his hand on the doorknob, he looked back at me. "There's no reason to tell your mother about this . . . right?"

I waved my hands. "Just go!" I smiled, and my Dad was gone.

Walking to the window, I pulled back the blind once again. I watched as Dad climbed in the car and then slowly backed out of the driveway. I watched the lights until the blowing snow swallowed the red glow.

I'd be on my mission in two weeks. In two years, I'd be back, and then who knows how long it would be before I was married and maybe having a baby of my own.

When it did happen, I was pretty sure I wouldn't be that calm.

I returned to the chair and the warm blanket.

Letterman was in rare form.

# Conversations in Fatherhood

7yo: "Dad? If somebody doesn't have any teeth, are they a toothless wonder?"

Dad: "Uh . . . sure."

7yo: "Ha! I knew it!"

Seven-year-old runs off.

Thirty seconds later.

5yo: "Dad? What do you call somebody who doesn't have any teeth?"

Dad: *Confused pause* "A toothless wonder."

5yo: "Ah, shucks."

# CHAPTER 13

I DRAGGED MY FEET ACROSS the steaming asphalt and then the hot cement. The impending burden already weighed heavily on my back. I paused before opening the door and squared my shoulders and took a deep breath.

*I can do this.*

I knew that was a lie, but I didn't have any options. I took one last breath and then held the door open.

"Come on, kids," I said. "Sacrament meeting starts in two minutes."

Normally I wasn't this apprehensive about attending sacrament meeting. Most days, I tried to enjoy it. But our ward had just experienced the perfect storm. It was like two high-pressure fronts converging in a single place and whipping up chaos until no one could hope to survive.

Front number one: our stake conference message. Stake conference was just one week prior. Reverence was the theme. There were many beautiful talks, but the one everyone would remember was our dear stake president's, whose kids were all grown up and out of the house. He stood up and told the parents of the stake that they had to do better at keeping their children under control during sacrament meeting. Not just to keep them quiet but to teach them reverence. To teach them to listen and learn. I knew this would all blow over in a month or two, but for now, all eyes would be on the families with children. And since I had eight children all under the age of fourteen, more than a fair share of eyes would be on our bench.

And our bench was usually a circus.

Front number two: one o'clock church. We'd had one o'clock church for seven months, but it hadn't gotten any easier. It was Ken's nap time, and he never slept in church. We'd tried everything with the rest of the kids. Made them play hard in the morning, made them rest. It didn't matter what we did. At 1:04, every single child got the wiggles and the giggles and the grumpies.

It didn't feel like worshiping. It felt like we were putting on a show.

I followed my kids into the church. Ken, the three-year-old, ran and did a headstand on the couch in the foyer, almost kicking Sister Johnson in the face. Margot, already mad at the world because she didn't like lunch and had therefore gone without, went over to chastise and only succeeded in making Ken scream. Ken expressed his displeasure by kicking Margot in the shins. We'd been in the church for eighteen seconds and already Margot was telling my wife she hated everybody and her nylons had a run.

I made a beeline for the chapel. I didn't like to herd kids from behind. I liked to think if I led the way, they would follow. It never really worked, but I was an eternal optimist.

The chapel doors seemed to say to me, *You really should just keep that whole mess on the outside, Brother.*

I entered the chapel and looked for a space. We needed room for at least eight people, although it worked better if we had space for ten. It helped if we could put space in between the kids to keep them from elbowing each other.

All the benches were packed.

I looked up at the bishop to see if he was whispering to a deacon to open the overflow. Luck wasn't with me. The bishop was whispering into an ear, but it wasn't a deacon's. It was the stake president's.

The stake president, who had given such a great talk on teaching kids to be reverent, was sitting on the stand where he could see the entire ward. And there was only one place to sit.

The front bench.

I almost turned around right then and there. But my wife was pushing me from behind, and Ken had already run into the chapel. Nothing to do but try to keep up.

The entire family was seated before the bishop got up to start the meeting. In looking back, that was the high point of the meeting and the only point on which I could gain solace—*at least we were on time.*

Like in Real Estate, reverence in sacrament meeting is all about location, location, location. When we had one child, reverence was easy. Two children, simply split them up. Three children was the last of the easy days. We could sit child, parent, child, parent, child. All was well.

But once we hit four, there was nothing to do but sit two kids together. Now that I had eight, it was hopeless. I couldn't even sit them in such a manner that I could whack the irreverent kids on the back of the head. Not that I could do any whacking with the stake president watching.

My wife and I had tried every combination we could come up with, but we'd never been able to find the sweet spot. No matter who sat next to whom, there were always problems.

Today was no exception. Before the end of the first song, Jeanette had pounded Kendra on the top of the head with a hymnal.

"But she was pointing at the words with her finger," Jeanette said when I pulled her away from Kendra. Luckily, the congregation was still singing, or everybody would have heard.

I whispered into her ear. "That's just how she reads. It helps her so she doesn't lose her place."

Jeanette glared at Kendra and then stuck her tongue out. I didn't dare look at the stake president.

After the invocation, my wife opened The Bag. Each week, we brought toys, books, magazines, and anything else that would keep the kids occupied. I'd argued that it only gave the kids something to fight over, but I'd never actually dared insist that we go into the meeting without The Bag. That was like jousting in your thermal underwear. The results could be very, very bad.

Books were passed down the aisle. Toys were grabbed and held protectively. It was touch and go for a moment, but then everybody settled down. I looked at the clock. We had to be halfway done by now.

Six minutes had passed.

I tried to slow my breathing. The bishop got up to cover ward business.

"Don't mess it up!" This came from Christy, and at least she was old enough to know that she shouldn't be yelling. Still, her hiss carried pretty well in the quiet chapel.

Ken was spinning a Rubix Cube that somebody had solved. Maybe Christy, since she seemed so passionate about not messing it up.

"Mine!" Ken wasn't old enough to know that he shouldn't be yelling.

I leaned forward and looked at Christy. She must have seen the pleading and desperation in my face. She rolled her eyes but sat back and folded her arms.

I felt sweat trickling down my back.

We sang another song, and then it was time for the sacrament.

A miracle. The sacrament passed with only one outburst. The children generally behaved themselves, but this time Chris put a sacrament cup in his mouth and blew. The cup sailed in a beautiful arc up and over three benches before it fell to the carpet somewhere behind us. I glared, but Chris was outside my zone of whacking.

The first speaker got up. Baby Rose needed a diaper change, and my wife left me. I tried to catch her eye, hoping she'd take a few more of the kids with her, but she avoided my gaze.

I looked down the aisle. Four kids to my left. Three kids to my right. I was outnumbered and outgunned.

Ken hit Jeanette on the leg. Jeanette hit him back. I grabbed Ken and put him on my lap. Ken leaned over to hit Jeanette again and only succeeded in smacking Cory, who up to this point had been fairly reverent.

Cory started crying, but it was a quiet cry, so I focused on Ken. I folded his arms and then wrapped my own arms around him and held him tight.

"Gah!" Ken yelled. "You're choking me!"

The speaker stopped. I could feel all eyes on me, although I knew none of them really suspected that I was choking my own son.

Not that I didn't want to.

"Ken," I said, loosening my grip. "You've got to be quiet, little buddy."

He squirmed out of my arms, and I didn't dare try to hold him tight. He'd won. I could only hope he'd be quiet wherever he ended up. In the meantime, I leaned over and tried to comfort Cory.

And then everybody was standing. We'd made it to the rest hymn. I felt a wave of hope. My wife would be back any time. The singing would mean my kids could wiggle and whisper and nobody would hear them for at least three minutes. I raised my voice in sincere thanks along with the rest of the congregation.

The song ended, and we all sat down. In the quiet stillness following the hymn and before the second speaker began, I heard Chris's voice from my far left.

"We *earned* that rest song."

He didn't speak loud enough for the entire congregation to hear. But I was pretty sure the first speaker heard, along with the stake president.

My wife came back. I roped in Ken and shoveled him off to her. I pulled Chris over to sit next to me.

The second speaker got up, and I realized it was a high councilor. I looked up at the clock. Twenty more minutes. My armpits felt damp.

Chris was wiggling at my side. I glanced over and saw that he was rolling up his tie. This was an old game I used to play to keep him quiet when he was little. It worked pretty well. I'd roll up my tie and tuck it under my chin. Then I'd hold both fingers out in front of me. Chris would try to make my fingers touch. When he did, I'd let the tie go and it would unroll in front of him. He got a big kick out of it.

Playing the tie trick was at least quiet. It took him several times before he even got the tie tucked up under his chin. When he finally did, he looked over to show me, and his tie promptly unrolled. I had to hide a smile. Another attempt, and Chris finally had the tie in its proper place.

Keeping his head down but his eyes up so he could see me, he held out one hand.

"Hey, Dad, pull my finger!"

I covered his mouth, but it was too late. He'd spoken loud enough that half the congregation must have heard it. My face burned, and I stared at the floor, hoping for an earthquake or a fire or diarrhea—anything that would give me an excuse to run for the exit.

No such luck.

The high councilor droned on. I kept shuffling kids, trying to find a reverent balance. My wife took three kids out, but it didn't seem to help. She brought them back in. Still, the second speaker went on. I couldn't bring myself to look at the stake president. I imagined his eyes boring into my scalp.

I looked up at the clock. Ten minutes after the hour. We were going into overtime! One minute. Two minutes. Three. By the time the closing song was over, we'd be a good eight minutes over.

Cory was two seats away from me. Usually she was relatively quiet, but it looked like she wanted to tell me something. I leaned over, and she leaned over too. She said something, but I didn't catch it. I shook my head to tell her I didn't understand. She spoke louder.

"This guy's wasting our time!"

I closed my eyes and winced. Her whisper had to have at least a ten-foot radius. I don't know if the high councilor heard her or not, but ten seconds later, he finished his talk and sat down. The hymn books came out, and the singing began. I studied the woodwork on the podium. I studied the plaster on the ceiling. The padding on the bench.

The singing stopped. The benediction was said. Finally, the congregation stood and started shuffling out of the chapel. My children raced off, running between legs and darting between bodies. I sat there in defeat.

I felt a hand on my shoulder. I turned my head and looked behind me. I caught white hair and a white mustache out of the corner or my eye. It was Brother Steele. A widower. All his kids had long since moved out of his home.

"You've got a mighty fine family there," he said. "Mighty fine, indeed."

I nodded. I thought about making a joke. Something about a circus or disturbing the peace or raging Mongolian hordes. But I couldn't. I closed my eyes. I saw my little kids. And my not so little kids. Growing up too fast. I saw myself sitting alone on a bench with my wife. Being able to focus on the meeting and the talks. That would be nice. That would be very nice.

But . . . this was nice too. And I wouldn't have it any other way.

# ABOUT THE AUTHOR

MATTHEW BUCKLEY IS THE PEN name of Marion Ray Jensen. He is the father of a small army of boys. He's a devoted beard wearer who enjoys running and bacon. Matthew lives in Utah, and he knows exactly who dealt it. He is always happy to hear from readers. You can e-mail him at marionjensen@gmail.com or visit his website at marionjensen. com.